# Poems About Love

**love** *luv, n* fondness; charity; an affection for something that gives pleasure; strong liking; devoted attachment to another person.

Thank you Vanessa Clarke
for inviting me to do this book
Thank you Hilary McGough
for helping me gather material
Thank you Suzanne Carnell
for the patient + cheerful editing
Thank you Poets.

Love,

Roger McGough.

# The Kingfisher Book of
# Poems About Love

Chosen by Roger McGough

*Illustrated by Chloë Cheese*

Kingfisher

KINGFISHER
An imprint of Larousse plc
Elsley House, 24-30 Great Titchfield Street
London W1P 7AD

First published by Kingfisher 1997

A CIP catalogue record for this book
is available from the British Library

ISBN 1 85677 384 0

Printed in Hong Kong

# CONTENTS

# LOVE
# COMES
# QUIETLY

## from AS I WALKED OUT ONE EVENING

I'll love you dear, I'll love you
  Till China and Africa meet
And the river jumps over the mountain
And the salmon sings in the street.

I'll love you till the ocean
  Is folded and hung up to dry
And the seven stars go squawking
  Like geese about in the sky.

W. H. AUDEN

## VALENTINE

My heart has made its mind up
And I'm afraid it's you.
Whatever you've got lined up,
My heart has made its mind up
And if you can't be signed up
This year, next year will do.
My heart has made its mind up
And I'm afraid it's you.

WENDY COPE

## IF LOVE WAS JAZZ

If love was jazz,
I'd be dazzled
By its razzmatazz.

If love was a sax
I'd melt in its brassy flame
Like wax.

If love was a guitar,
I'd pluck its six strings,
Eight to the bar.

If love was a trombone,
I'd feel its slow
Slide, right down my backbone.

If love was a drum,
I'd be caught in its snare,
Kept under its thumb.

If love was a trumpet,
I'd blow it.

If love was jazz,
I'd sing its praises,
Like Larkin has.

But love isn't jazz.
It's an organ recital.
Eminently worthy,
Not nearly as vital.

If love was jazz,
I'd always want more.
I'd be a regular
On that smoky dance-floor.

LINDA FRANCE

# SOME SAY THAT
# LOVE'S A LITTLE BOY

Some say that love's a little boy,
    And some say it's a bird,
Some say it makes the world go round,
    And some say that's absurd,
And when I asked the man next-door,
    Who looked as if he knew,
His wife got very cross indeed,
    And said it wouldn't do.

    Does it look like a pair of pyjamas,
Or the ham in a temperance hotel?
    Does its odour remind one of llamas,
Or has it a comforting smell?
    Is it prickly to touch as a hedge is,
Or soft as eiderdown fluff?
    Is it sharp or quite smooth at the edges?
    O tell me the truth about love.

Our history books refer to it
        In cryptic little notes,
It's quite a common topic on
        The Transatlantic boats;
I've found the subject mentioned in
        Accounts of suicides,
And even seen it scribbled on
        The backs of railway-guides.

Does it howl like a hungry Alsatian,
        Or boom like a military band?
Could one give a first-rate imitation
        On a saw or a Steinway Grand?
Is its singing at parties a riot?
        Does it only like Classical stuff?
Will it stop when one wants to be quiet?
        O tell me the truth about love.

I looked inside the summer-house;
        It wasn't ever there:
I tried the Thames at Maidenhead,
        And Brighton's bracing air.
I don't know what the blackbird sang,
        Or what the tulip said;
But it wasn't in the chicken-run,
        Or underneath the bed.

Can it pull extraordinary faces?
　　Is it usually sick on a swing?
Does it spend all its time at the races,
　　or fiddling with pieces of string?
Has it views of its own about money?
　　Does it think Patriotism enough?
Are its stories vulgar but funny?
　　O tell me the truth about love.

When it comes, will it come without warning
　　Just as I'm picking my nose?
Will it knock on my door in the morning,
　　Or tread in the bus on my toes?
Will it come like a change in the weather?
　　Will its greeting be courteous or rough?
Will it alter my life altogether?
　　O tell me the truth about love.

**W. H. AUDEN**

# WHAT WE MIGHT BE, WHAT WE ARE

If you were a scoop of vanilla
And I were the cone where you sat,
If you were a slowly pitched baseball
And I were the swing of a bat,

If you were a shiny new fishhook
And I were a bucket of worms,
If we were a pin and a pincushion,
We might be on intimate terms.

If you were a plate of spaghetti
And I were your piping-hot sauce,
We'd not even need to write letters
To put our affection across.

But you're just a piece of red ribbon
In the beard of a Balinese goat
And I'm a New Jersey mosquito.
I guess we'll stay slightly remote.

X. J. KENNEDY

## FIRST DATE

When you race home from school,
    With your hair all askew,
You've loads of revision,
    And homework to do,
When all that is finished,
    You shampoo your hair,
Then dry it, and style it,
    With slow loving care,
You've barely got time,
    For a quick bite to eat,
Before you can change,
    Into something quite neat,
But it's got to look modern,
    And feminine too,
Then when you've changed,
    There's your make-up to do,
And now that your face,
    Is looking just right,
You glance in the mirror,
    Wow! what a sight!

He'll never resist you,
    You don't think he'll try,
Your heart beats loudly,
    Your spirits run high,
You look out the window,
    He's there at the gate,
And you hurry downstairs,
    To your very first date.

SUSAN WHYTE

## BOY   GIRL

| Boy | Girl |
|---|---|
| Garden | Gate |
| Standing | Kissing |
| Very | Late |
| Dad | Comes |
| Big | Boots |
| Boy | Runs |
| Girl | Scoots |

ANON

# GROWING UP

## ONE UP

It feels good to be up
at the top of a tree
or about on a hill
looking out.

There's a thrill
up a tree
or a hill.
It's good to be me.

## TWO UP

It's great being us
side by side
on the bus.
I don't care what they say.

Let me pay.

JANE WHITTLE

# HOW TO TALK

It was on the ferris wheel
I was introduced to

the art of conversation.
She was thirteen,

I was fourteen;
many times we passed the point where we'd climbed on.

How high it is, up here, she said
when we were near the top.

I could see my name
on the tip of her tongue.

ANDREW JOHNSTON

# WORDS, WIDE NIGHT

Somewhere on the other side of this wide night
and the distance between us, I am thinking of you.
The room is turning slowly away from the moon.

This is pleasurable. Or shall I cross that out and say
it is sad? In one of the tenses I singing
an impossible song of desire that you cannot hear.

La lala la. See? I close my eyes and imagine
the dark hills I would have to cross
to reach you. For I am in love with you and this

is what it is like or what it is like in words.

CAROL ANN DUFFY

20

## LAKE OF BAYS

"Well, I'm not chicken . . ."
that skinny ten-year-old girl
balanced on the crazy-high railing
of the Dorset bridge:

                    suddenly let go

down

fifty feet into the water.

"That one will never grow up
to be a lady," my mother said
as we walked away.

but I'll remember
her brown body dropping like a stone
long after I've forgotten
many many ladies . . .

RAYMOND SOUSTER

# I WILL MAKE YOU BROOCHES

I will make you brooches and toys for your delight
Of bird-song at morning and star-shine at night.
I will make a palace fit for you and me
Of green days in forests and blue days at sea.

I will make my kitchen, and you shall keep your room,
Where white flows the river and bright blows the broom,
And you shall wash your linen and keep your body white
In rainfall at morning and dewfall at night.

And this shall be for music when no one else is near,
The fine song for singing, the rare song to hear!
That only I remember, that only you admire,
Of the broad road that stretches and the roadside fire.

ROBERT LOUIS STEVENSON

# A LOVE SONG TO EROS

You're a smasher and a smiler and a triple turning dive,
The somersaulting intellect inside the thing alive.
You duck, and twist, and toss, and swim the raging sea,
A finger in my mind, like a spoon in tea.

There's murder in the boardroom, death in every nerve,
The evil get more evil and what the good deserve.
Rape, starvation, age and pain, sorrow and disease,
And people pray to you, dear god, the all-time tease.

You're a honey in the morning. You're never twice the same.
There's not a soul I know to hope to scandalize your name.
Let's have a drink beside the fire. I'll walk you down the street.
We'll split up by the water-wheel and swear we'll never meet.

We'll meet of course tonight and feel the tender spark
Illuminate our loving in the blissful dark.

SEBASTIAN BARKER

# THE MASKS OF LOVE

I come in from a walk
with you
and they ask me
if it is raining.

I didn't notice
but I'll have to give them
the right answer
or they'll think I'm crazy.

ALDEN NOWLAN

# LOVE COMES QUIETLY

Love comes quietly,
finally, drops
about me, on me,
in the old ways.

What did I know
thinking myself
able to go
alone all the way.

ROBERT CREELEY

# TELEPHONE

The telephone
is a creature
that springs

It sleeps
as lightly
as a cat
and leaps
on you
when your back
is turned

I used to think
it is a pest
how it buzzes
and rings
But now miles from you

I place
this creature
to my ear

and my heart sings

JOHN AGARD

# THE VOYEUR

what's your favourite word dearie

is it wee

I hope it's wee

wee's such a nice wee word

like a wee hairy dog

with two wee eyes

such a nice wee word to play with dearie

you can say it quickly

with a wee smile

and a wee glance to the side

or you can say it slowly dearie

with your mouth a wee bit open

and a wee sigh dearie

a wee sigh

put your wee head on my shoulder dearie

oh my

a great wee word

and Scottish

it makes you proud

TOM LEONARD

# LOVE POEMS

Life's
Old
Vast
Emotion

Lips
Of
Venus
Expectant

Lots
Of
Valentines'
Envelopes

Luton
Oh
Veritable
Enigma

JOHN HEGLEY

## SHE LOVES ME

she loves me
she loves me not
she loves
she loves me
she
she loves

she

EMMETT WILLIAMS

## egotist

I
only have
I I I I
for
u.

BERNARD PROCTOR

# I'VE GOT A GAL IN KALAMAZOO

A-B-C-D-E-F-G-H
I got a gal in Kalamazoo
don't wanna boast but I know she's the toast
of Kalamazoo zoo zoo zoo zoo zoo.

Years have gone by,
my, my, how she grew,
I liked her looks, when I carried her books
in Kalamazoo zoo zoo zoo zoo.

I'm gonna send a wire,
hoppin' on a flyer, leavin' today.
Am I dreamin' I can hear her screamin'
"Hya Mister Jackson". Ev'rything's O
K-A-L-A-M-A-Z-O

Oh, what a gal, a real pipper-oo;
I'll make a bid for that freckle faced kid
I'm hurrying to.
I'm going to Michigan to see the sweetest gal
in Kalamazoo zoo zoo zoo zoo zoo!
Kalamazoo!

MACK GORDON

# THE ORANGE

At lunchtime I bought a huge orange –
The size of it made us all laugh.
I peeled it and shared it with Robert and Dave –
They got quarters and I had a half.

And that orange, it made me so happy,
As ordinary things often do
Just lately. The shopping. A walk in the park.
This is peace and contentment. It's new.

The rest of the day was quite easy.
I did all the jobs on my list
And enjoyed them and had some time over.
I love you. I'm glad I exist.

WENDY COPE

## PEOPLE

Some people talk and talk
and never say a thing.
Some people look at you
and birds begin to sing.

Some people laugh and laugh
and yet you want to cry.
Some people touch your hand
and music fills the sky.

CHARLOTTE ZOLOTOW

# GIVE ME A HOUSE

Give me a house, said Polly.
Give me land, said Hugh.
Give me the moon, said Sadie.
Give me the sun, said Sue.

Give me a horse, said Rollo.
Give me a hound, said Joe.
Give me fine linen, said Sarah.
Give me silk, said Flo.

Give me a mountain, said Kirsty.
Give me a valley, said Jim.
Give me a river, said Dodo.
Give me the sky, said Tim.

Give me the ocean, said Adam.
Give me a ship, said Hal.
Give me a kingdom, said Rory.
Give me a crown, said Sal.

Give me gold, said Peter.
Give me silver, said Paul.
Give me love, said Jenny,
Or nothing at all.

**CHARLES CAUSLEY**

# IF YOU CALL ME

As gingko leaves, yellowed in autumn,
dance and toss in the wind,
    so I will come to you
    if you call me, my love.

As the new moon moves over the hills silently
at night when a lake is veiled in mist,
    so I will come to you
    if you call me, my love.

As the water meanders at the edge of heaven
under the soft-melted spring sky,
    so I will come to you
    if you call me, my love.

As the sun soaks into the lawn in early season
when egrets sing out through the bright air,
    so I will come to you
    if you call me, my love.

SIN SŎK-CHŎNG

# CHERRIES

"I'll never speak to Jamie again" –
Cried Jennie, "let alone wed,
No, not till blackbirds' wings grow white,
And crab-apple trees grow cherries for spite,
But I'll marry Percy instead."

But Jamie met her that self-same day,
Where crab-apple trees outspread,
And poured out his heart like a man insane,
And argued until he became profane,
That he never meant what he said.

Now strange as it seems, the truth must be told,
So wildly Jamie pled,
That cherries came out where the crab-apples grew,
And snow-winged blackbirds came down from the blue,
And feasted overhead.

E. J. PRATT

## LOVE POEM

I live in you, you live in me;
We are two gardens haunted by each other.
Sometimes I cannot find you there,
There is only the swing creaking, that you have just left,
Or your favourite book beside the sundial.

DOUGLAS DUNN

# WHO LOVES YOU

I worry about you travelling in those mystical machines.
Every day people fall from the clouds, dead.
Breathe in and out and in and out easy.
Safety, safely, safe home.

Your photograph is in the fridge, smiles when the light
     comes on.
All the time people are burnt in the public places.
Rest where the cool trees drop to a gentle shade.
Safety, safely, safe home.

Don't lie down on the sands where the hole in the sky is.
Too many people being gnawed to shreds.
Send me your voice however it comes across oceans.
Safety, safely, safe home.

The loveless men and homeless boys are out there and angry.
Nightly people end their lives in the shortcut.
Walk in the light, steadily hurry towards me.
Safety, safely, safe home. (Who loves you?)
Safety, safely, safe home.

CAROL ANN DUFFY

# COME AWAY, MY LOVE

Come away, my love, from streets
Where unkind eyes divide,
And shop windows reflect our difference.
In the shelter of my faithful room, rest.

There, safe from opinions, being behind
Myself, I can see only you;
And in my dark eyes your grey
Will dissolve.

　　The candlelight throws
Two dark shadows on the wall
Which merge into one as I close beside you.

When at last the lights are out,
And I feel your hand in mind,
Two human breaths join in one,
And the piano weaves
Its unchallenged harmony.

JOSEPH KARIUKI

37

## PAST TIME

I believe we came together
Out of ignorance not love,
Both being shy and hunted in the city.
In the hot summer, touching each other,
Amazed at how love could come
Like a waterfall, with frightening force
And bruising sleep. Waking at noon,
Touching each other for direction,
Out of ignorance not love.

HARVEY SHAPIRO

## REASONS

Sweet one I love you
for your lovely shape,
for the art you make
in paint and bed and rhyme,
but most because we see
into each other's hearts,
there to read secrets
and to trust,
and cancel time.

TOM McGRATH

## SUNDAY

The mint bed is in
bloom: lavender haze
day. The grass is
more than green and
throws up sharp and
cutting lights to
slice through the
plane tree leaves. And
on the cloudless blue
I scribble your name.

JAMES SCHUYLER


## THE SENSATION OF WELL-BEING

The sensation of well-being,
   Which my heart from yours receives,
Is like the deep content a tree
   Finds in its fresh green leaves.

FARRUKHI

# A SPELL TO MAKE
# A GOOD TIME LAST

Walk with your lover through a doorway
Walk with your lover through the maytime sunlight
Walk with your lover by a lake

The past is a stone for playing ducks and drakes
The stone is lying at your feet
Skim the stone away across the lake

The future is a stone for playing ducks and drakes
The stone is lying at your feet
Skim the stone away across the lake

Lie down beside the water
Lie down beside your lover
Lie down beside the water
Lie down beside your lover

ADRIAN MITCHELL

# SEVEN WISHES

Why can't I be the band that binds your forehead,
so close to your thoughts?

Why can't I be the nub of sweetcorn
you shred with your wildcat's teeth?

Why can't I be the turquoise round your neck
warmed by the storm of your blood?

Why can't I be the thread of many colours
that slides through your fingers on the loom?

Why can't I be the velvet tunic
over the ebb and flow of your heart?

Why can't I be the sand in your moccasins
that dares to stroke your toes?

Why can't I be your night's dream
when you moan in the black arms of sleep?

ANON (PUEBLO INDIAN)

# THE GLOVE AND
THE GUITAR

A toy guitar
And an old green glove
Meeting on the rubbish dump
Fell in love.

"How smooth, how plump,
How curved you are,"
Said the old green glove
To the toy guitar.

Said the toy guitar,
"My dusty heart sings
When I think of your fingers
Tickling my strings."

Dusk and darkness
And, oh, what a fright
The neighbourhood tom-cats
Got that night,

When they heard from the dump
Strange sounds coming,
Sounds of plucking,
Sounds of strumming,

Sounds of a wild
Flamenco tune,
As the glove and the toy guitar
Played beneath the moon.

**RICHARD EDWARDS**

# RIDDLE-ME-REE

My first is in life (not contained within heart)
My second's in whole but never in part.
My third's in forever, but also in vain.
My last's in ending, why not in pain?

LIZ LOCHHEAD

# FIRST
# FROST

# DOWN WITH LOVE

Down with love,
The flowers and rice and shoes,
Down with love
The root of all midnight blues.
Down with things that give you that well known pain.
Take that moon and wrap it in cellophane
Down with love,
Let's liquidate all its friends
Moon and June and Roses and Rainbows' ends.
Down with songs that moan about night and day;
Down with love,
Yes, take it away, away
Away, take it away.
Give it back to the birds and the bees and the Viennese,
Down with eyes romantic and stupid.
Down with sighs, down with Cupid.
Brother, let's stuff that Dove.
Down with love! Love!

E. Y. HARBURG

## OH, WHEN I WAS
## IN LOVE WITH YOU

Oh, when I was in love with you,
    Then I was clean and brave,
And miles around the wonder grew
    How well did I behave.

And now the fancy passes by,
    And nothing will remain,
And miles around they'll say that I
    Am quite myself again.

A. E. HOUSMAN

# SAMOOREENA

When Samooreena went away
Milk turned sour and grass turned grey,
Come home, Samooreena.

When Samooreena went away
Tortoises stayed in all day,
Poets couldn't find one rhyme,
Climbing roses didn't climb,
Come home, Samooreena.

When Samooreena went away
Garden hoses wouldn't play,
Birds, instead of singing, wailed,
Clocks ran down, the harvest failed,
Toast went soggy, soup got lumps,
Maude got measles, I got mumps,
Come home, Samooreena.

Now she's back! Oh, Samooreena,
Blades of grass were never greener,
Tortoises stretch out and run
Faster than rabbits in the sun,
Poets cry "Ah! Spoon and June!"

Climbing roses brush the moon,
Hoses gush and spout and stream,
Toast's like crackling, soup's like cream,
Wheat's all ears, the milk tastes sweet,
Clocks go tick-tock, birds tweet-tweet,
Maude, unmeasled, skips, while I
Mumpless on my soapbox cry
"Samooreena, Samooreena,
Stay here, Samooreena!"

RICHARD EDWARDS

# THE BALLAD OF
# CAMDEN TOWN

I walked with Maisie long years back
The streets of Camden Town,
I splendid in my suit of black,
And she divine in brown.

Hers was a proud and noble face,
A secret heart, and eyes
Like water in a lonely place
Beneath unclouded skies.

A bed, a chest, a faded mat,
And broken chairs a few,
Were all we had to grace our flat
In Hazel Avenue.

But I could walk to Hampstead Heath,
And crown her head with daisies,
And watch the streaming world beneath,
And men with other Maisies.

When I was ill and she was pale
And empty stood our store,
She left the latchkey on its nail,
And saw me nevermore.

Perhaps she cast herself away
Lest both of us should drown.
Perhaps she feared to die, as they
Who die in Camden Town.

What came of her? The bitter nights
Destroy the rose and lily,
And souls are lost among the lights
Of painted Piccadilly.

What came of her? The river flows
So deep and wide and stilly,
And waits to catch the fallen rose
And clasp the broken lily.

I dream she dwells in London still
And breathes the evening air,
And often walk to Primrose Hill,
And hope to meet her there.

Once more together we will live,
For I will find her yet:
I have so little to forgive;
So much I can't forget.

JAMES ELROY FLECKER

## ADRIAN HENRI'S TALKING
## AFTER CHRISTMAS BLUES

Well I woke up this mornin' it was Christmas Day
And the birds were singing the night away
I saw my stocking lying on the chair
Looked right to the bottom but you weren't there
there was
    apples
        oranges
            chocolates
                . . . aftershave


– but no you.


So I went downstairs and the dinner was fine
There was pudding and turkey and lots of wine
And I pulled those crackers with a laughing face
Till I saw there was no one in your place
there was
    mincepies
        brandy
            nuts and raisins
                . . . mashed potato
– but no you.

Now it's New Year and it's Auld Lang Syne
And it's 12 o'clock and I'm feeling fine
Should Auld Acquaintance be Forgot?
I don't know girl, but it hurts a lot
there was
    whisky
        vodka
            dry Martini (stirred
                but not shaken)
. . . and 12 New Year resolutions
– all of them about you.

So it's all the best for the year ahead
As I stagger upstairs and into bed
Then I looked at the pillow by my side
. . . I tell you baby I almost cried
there'll be
    Autumn
        Summer
            Spring
                . . . and Winter
– all of them without you.

ADRIAN HENRI

## A BLADE OF GRASS

You ask for a poem.
I offer you a blade of grass.
You say it is not good enough.
You ask for a poem.

I say this blade of grass will do.
It has dressed itself in frost,
It is more immediate
Than any image of my making.

You say it is not a poem,
It is a blade of grass and grass
Is not quite good enough.
I offer you a blade of grass.

You are indignant.
You say it is too easy to offer grass.
It is absurd.
Anyone can offer a blade of grass.

You ask for a poem.
And so I write you a tragedy about
How a blade of grass
Becomes more and more difficult to offer,

And about how as you grow older
A blade of grass
Becomes more difficult to accept.

BRIAN PATTEN

# FIRST FROST

In the telephone booth a girl
is turning into ice.
Huddled in a thin coat
her face is tear-stained
and smeared with lipstick.

She wears earrings made out of glass
and breathes on to fingers that freeze.

She will have to go home now.
Alone along the icy street.

First frost. A beginning of losses.
The first frost of telephone phrases.

Winter glistens on her cheek.
The first frost of having been hurt.

ANDREI VOZNESENSKY

## AWAY FROM YOU

away from you
i feel a great emptiness
a gnawing loneliness

with you
i get that reassuring feeling
of wanting to escape

ROGER McGOUGH


## WHEN YOU'RE AWAY

When you're away, I'm restless, lonely,
Wretched, bored, dejected; only
Here's the rub, my darling dear,
I feel the same when you are near.

SAMUEL HOFFENSTEIN

# WHERE HAVE YOU GONE

Where have you gone

with your confident
walk with
your crooked smile

why did you leave
me
when you took your
laughter
and departed

are you aware that
with you
went the sun
all light
and what few stars
there were?

where have you gone
with your confident
walk your
crooked smile the
rent money
in one pocket and
my heart
in another . . .

MARI EVANS

# ONE PERFECT ROSE

A single flow'r he sent me, since we met.
  All tenderly his messenger he chose;
Deep-hearted, pure, with scented dew still wet—
  One perfect rose.

I knew the language of the floweret;
  "My fragile leaves," it said, "his heart enclose."
Love long has taken for his amulet
  One perfect rose.

Why is it no one ever sent me yet
  One perfect limousine, do you suppose?
Ah no, it's always just my luck to get
  One perfect rose.

DOROTHY PARKER

# MY LOVE IS LIKE
# A RED RED ROSE

My love is like a red red rose
Her beauty makes you stare,
She stands alone near garden lawns
While bees hum in her hair.

My love is like a red red rose
Her body's green and thin,
And when I try to squeeze her waist
She sticks her prickles in.

My love is like a red red rose
She's wilting by the hour,
It makes no sense to fall in love
With someone like a flower.

STEVE TURNER

# JULIET

How did the party go in Portman Square?
I cannot tell you, Juliet was not there.

And how did Lady Gaster's party go?
Juliet was next to me and I do not know.

# THE FRAGMENT

Towards the evening of her splendid day
Those who are little children now shall say
(Finding this verse), "Who wrote it, Juliet?"
And Juliet answer gently, "I forget."

HILAIRE BELLOC

# MIDDLE-AGED CONVERSATION

"Are you sad to think how often
   You have let all wisdom go
For a crimson mouth and rounded
   Thighs and eyes you drowned in?" "No."

"Do you find this level country,
   Where the winds more gently blow,
Better than the summit raptures
   And the deep-sea sorrows?" "No."

A. S. J. TESSIMOND

## INTO MY HEART
## AN AIR THAT KILLS

Into my heart an air that kills
    From yon far country blows:
What are those blue remembered hills,
    What spires, what farms are those?

That is the land of lost content,
    I see it shining plain,
The happy highways where I went
    And cannot come again.

A. E. HOUSMAN


## SONG FOR A BEAUTIFUL GIRL
## PETROL-PUMP ATTENDANT
## ON THE MOTORWAY

I wanted your soft verges
But you gave me the hard shoulder.

ADRIAN HENRI

# YESTERDAY GIRL

I remember her face (I think)
and a summer evening
standing on the shore
watching the Mersey
turning in its sleep
and the seagulls crying
sliding down the sky
like kids on banisters
while we wrote
I love you
in the sweaty summer sand
with sticks
and skipped across rocks
and both held hands
to keep from falling
out of love

But we couldn't

RICHARD HILL

# IT'S ONCE I COURTED
# AS PRETTY A LASS

It's once I courted as pretty a lass,
    As ever your eyes did see;
But now she's come to such a pass,
    She never will do for me.
She invited me to her house,
    Where oft I'd been before,
And she tumbled me into the hog-tub,
    And I'll never go there any more.

ANON

# BECOMING
# WHAT
# WE ARE

## SPRING

Snow melts,
    and the village is overflowing –
      with the children.

ISSA

## POEM FOR NTOMBE IAYO
## (AT FIVE WEEKS OF AGE)

who them people think
they are putting
me down here
on this floor

i'll just lay
here stretching
my arms and maybe i'll kick
my legs a li'l bit

why i betcha i'll just get up
from here and walk
soons i get big

NIKKI GIOVANNI

# NURSERY DAYS

We were innocent
And frivolous and
Had some good games,
But I wondered what those
Big ladies who would hang around
Got out of it.

ROBERT SHURE

# THE FAT LADY'S REQUEST

I, too, will disappear, will
Escape into centuries of darkness.

Come here and give me a cuddle,
Sit on my lap and give me a hug

While we are both still enjoying
This mysterious whirling planet.

And if you find me fat, you find me
Also, easy to find, very easy to find.

JOYCE LA VERNE

# GIVE YOURSELF A HUG

Give yourself a  hug
when you feel unloved

Give yourself a hug
when people put on airs
to make you feel a bug

Give yourself a hug
when everyone seems to give you
a cold-shoulder shrug

Give yourself a hug –
a big big hug

And keep on singing,
"Only one in a million like me
Only one in a million-billion-thrillion-zillion
like me."

GRACE NICHOLS

# ZEROING IN

The tree down the street
   has little green apples
      that never get bigger
         never turn red.
They just drop on the ground
   get worm holes
      brown spots.
They're
   just right for stepping on
      like walking on bumpy marbles,
         or green eggs that break with a snap
            just right for gathering
               in a heap behind the hedge
               waiting
                  for a target.
Here comes my brother.

DIANE DAWBER

# I'M DISGUSTED
# WITH MY BROTHER

I'm disgusted with my brother,
I am positively sore,
I have never been so angry
with a human being before,
he's everything detestable
that's spelled with A through Z,
he deserves to be the target
of a ten-pound bumblebee.

I'd like to wave a magic wand
and make him disappear,
or watch a wild rhinoceros
attack him from the rear,
perhaps I'll cook a pot of soup
and dump my brother in,
he forgot today's my birthday –
oh, how could he . . . he's my *twin*!

JACK PRELUTSKY

# THE QUARREL

I quarrelled with my brother
I don't know what about,
One thing led to another
And somehow we fell out.
The start of it was slight,
The end of it was strong,
He said he was right,
I knew he was wrong!

We hated one another.
The afternoon turned black.
Then suddenly my brother
Thumped me on the back,
And said, "Oh, *come* along!
We can't go on all night –
I was in the wrong."
So he was in the right.

ELEANOR FARJEON

# ME

My Mum is on a diet,
My Dad is on the booze,
My Gran's out playing Bingo
And she was born to lose.

My brother's stripped his motorbike
Although it's bound to rain.
My sister's playing Elton John
Over and over again.

What a dim old family!
What a dreary lot!
Sometimes I think that I'm the only
Superstar they've got.

KIT WRIGHT

## THERE WAS A MAN

There was a man who never was.
This tragedy occurred because
His parents, being none too smart,
Were born two hundred years apart.

DENNIS LEE

## THE PARENT

Children aren't happy with nothing to ignore,
And that's what parents were created for.

OGDEN NASH

# YOUNG

A thousand doors ago
when I was a lonely kid
in a big house with four
garages and it was summer
as long as I could remember,
I lay on the lawn at night
clover wrinkling under me,
my mother's window a funnel
of yellow heat running out,
my father's window, half shut,
an eye where sleepers pass,
and the boards of the house
were smooth and white as wax
and probably a million leaves
sailed on their strange stalks
as the crickets ticked together,
and I, in my brand new body,
which was not a woman's yet,
told the stars my questions
and thought God could really see
the heat and the painted light,
elbows, knees, dreams, goodnight.

ANNE SEXTON

# AUTOBIOGRAPHIA
# LITERARIA

When I was a child
I played by myself in a
corner of the schoolyard
all alone.

I hated dolls and I
hated games, animals were
not friendly and birds
flew away.

If anyone was looking
for me I hid behind a
tree and cried out "I am
an orphan."

And here I am, the
centre of all beauty!
writing these poems!
Imagine!

FRANK O'HARA

# POEM FOR A DAUGHTER

"I think I'm going to have it,"
I said, joking between pains.
The midwife rolled competent
sleeves over corpulent milky arms.
"Dear, you never have it,
we deliver it."
A judgement years proved true.
Certainly I've never had you

as you still have me, Caroline.
Why does a mother need a daughter?
Heart's needle, hostage to fortune,
freedom's end. Yet nothing's more perfect
than that bleating, razor-shaped cry
that delivers a mother to her baby.
The bloodcord snaps that held
their sphere together. The child,
tiny and alone, creates the mother.

A woman's life is her own
until it is taken away
by a first particular cry.
Then she is not alone
but part of the premises
of everything there is:
a time, a tribe, a war.
When we belong to the world
we become what we are.

ANNE STEVENSON

# BEATTIE IS THREE

At the top of the stairs
I ask for her hand. OK.
She gives it to me.
How her fist fits my palm,
A bunch of consolation.
We take our time
Down the steep carpetway
As I wish silently
That the stairs were endless.

ADRIAN MITCHELL

## TO MY DAUGHTER

Bright clasp of her whole hand around my finger,
My daughter, as we walk together now.
All my life I'll feel a ring invisibly
Circle this bone with shining: when she is grown
Far from today as her eyes are far already.

STEPHEN SPENDER


## SONG FOR AN INNOCENT

Born with such gentleness as you,
with such a pure and trusting face,
how could I tell you what I knew? –
this world is not your kind of place.

Your candid look, your artless grace
fit you for somewhere else than here.
This world is not your kind of place.
I wish it were. I wish it were.

EVANGELINE PATERSON

# SWEET SONG FOR KATIE

The white doves are cooing,
Oh! Katie my dear,
In the sun in the morning,
In the spring of the year.
The peace doves are cooing,
Oh! Kate can you hear?

And when you are grown
And summer is high,
Will you listen my darling
To the birds in the sky,
And spread out your wild arms
As if you could fly?

Oh! I ask nothing better
For Katie and me
That we're brave as the new wind
That springs from the sea,
And we sing like the peace doves
In the green mango tree.

For we'll build a new world,
When the cane grass is high,
And peace will drop softly
Like wings from the sky,
And the children will run,
And the wild birds will fly.

And all that I ask now
For Katie and me,
Is a faith that is strong
As the wind off the sea,
Blowing so loud
In the green mango tree,
With a song that is ceaseless
As a dove in a tree.

DOROTHY HEWETT

# A CHILD HALF-ASLEEP

Stealthily parting the small-hours silence,
a hardly-embodied figment of his brain
comes down to sit with me
as I work late.
Flat-footed, as though his legs and feet
were still asleep.

On a stool,
staring into the fire,
his dummy dangling.

Fire ignites the small coals of his eyes;
it stares back through the holes
into his head, into the darkness.

I ask what woke him.

"A wolf dreamed me," he says.

TONY CONNOR

# BEARHUG

Griffin calls to come and kiss him goodnight
I yell OK. Finish something I'm doing,
then something else, walk slowly round
the corner to my son's room.
He is standing arms outstretched
waiting for a bearhug. Grinning.

Why do I give my emotion an animal's name,
give it that dark squeeze of death?
This is the hug which collects
all his small bones and his warm neck against me.
The thin tough body under the pyjamas
locks to me like a magnet of blood.

How long was he standing there
like that, before I came?

MICHAEL ONDAATJE

# BEARHUGS

Whenever my sons call round we hug each other.
Bearhugs. Both bigger than me and stronger
They lift me off my feet, crushing the life out of me.

They smell of oil paint and aftershave, of beer
Sometimes and tobacco, and of women
Whose memory they seem reluctant to wash away.

They haven't lived with me for years,
Since they were tiny, and so each visit
Is an assessment, a reassurance of love unspoken.

I look for some resemblance to my family.
Seize on an expression, a lifted eyebrow,
A tilt of the head, but cannot see myself.

Though like each other, they are not like me.
But I can see in them something of my father.
Uncles, home on leave during the war.

At three or four, I loved those straightbacked men
Towering above me, smiling and confident.
The whole world before them. Or so it seemed.

I look at my boys, slouched in armchairs
They have outgrown. See Tom in army uniform
And Finn in air force blue. Time is up.

Bearhugs. They lift me off my feet
And fifty years fall away. One son
After another, crushing the life into me.

ROGER McGOUGH

# CINDERS

After the pantomime, carrying you back to the car
On the coldest night of the year
My coat, black leather, cracking in the wind.

Through the darkness we are guided by a star
It is the one the Good Fairy gave you
You clutch it tightly, your magic wand.

And I clutch you tightly for fear you blow away
For fear you grow up too soon and – suddenly,
I almost slip, so take it steady down the hill.

Hunched against the wind and hobbling
I could be mistaken for your grandfather
And sensing this, I hold you tighter still.

Knowing that I will never see you dressed for the Ball
Be on hand to warn you against Prince Charmings
And the happy ever afters of pantomime.

On reaching the car I put you into the baby seat
And fumble with straps I have yet to master
Thinking, if only there were more time. More time.

You are crying now. Where is your wand?
Oh no. I can't face going back for it
Let some kid find it in tomorrow's snow.

Waiting in the wings, the witching hour.
Already the car is changing. Smells sweet
Of ripening seed. We must go. Must go.

ROGER McGOUGH

# FIRST LESSON

The thing to remember about fathers is, they're men.
A girl has to keep it in mind.
They are dragon-seekers, bent on improbable rescues.
Scratch any father, you find
Someone chock-full of qualms and romantic terrors,
Believing change is a threat –
Like your first shoes with heels on, like your first bicycle
It took such months to get.

Walk in strange woods, they warn you about the snakes there.
Climb, and they fear you'll fall.
Books, angular boys, or swimming in deep water –
Fathers mistrust them all.
Men are the worriers. It is difficult for them
To learn what they must learn:
How you have a journey to take and very likely,
For a while, will not return.

PHYLLIS McGINLEY

# A GOOD IDEA FOR
# WINTRY WEATHER

At breakfast in the dark I pop
my dad's hat over the teapot
so that his head shall be hot
though the full buses pass his stop.

LIBBY HOUSTON

# THANK YOU, DAD,
# FOR EVERYTHING

Thank you for laying the carpet, Dad,
Thank you for showing us how,
But what is that lump in the middle, Dad?
And why is it saying mia-ow?

DOUG MACLEOD

# I SEE YOU DANCING, FATHER

No sooner downstairs after the night's rest
And in the door
Than you started to dance a step
In the middle of the kitchen floor.

And as you danced
You whistled.
You made your own music
Always in tune with yourself.

Well, nearly always, anyway.
You're buried now
In Lislaughtin Abbey
And whenever I think of you

I go back beyond the old man
Mind and body broken
To find the unbroken man.
It is the moment before the dance begins,

Your lips are enjoying themselves
Whistling an air.
Whatever happens or cannot happen
In the time I have to spare
I see you dancing, father.

BRENDAN KENNELLY

# MY PAPA'S WALTZ

The whiskey on your breath
Could make a small boy dizzy;
But I hung on like death:
Such waltzing was not easy.

We romped until the pans
Slid from the kitchen shelf;
My mother's countenance
Could not unfrown itself.

The hand that held my wrist
Was battered on one knuckle;
At every step you missed
My right ear scraped a buckle.

You beat time on my head
With a palm caked hard by dirt,
Then waltzed me off to bed
Still clinging to your shirt.

**THEODORE ROETHKE**

# DANCING ON TOES

Round the kitchen on the rag rug
We reeled. Me standing on my mother's toes
Gripping her pinny fast, my nose
Dug in the soft pillow of her belly. Smug

Old Mushy Cat watched from on top
The sewing machine, disdainful, proud.
We turned the volume knob up loud
And danced and danced until the music stopped.

Then, years on years, around I danced
In my mother's kitchen with *my* child balanced
On my toes. Wildly we hopped, higher
We turned the music, and spun turning

And turning, and I looked in the coal fire
And saw suddenly twenty-odd years burning.

MIKE HARDING

# THE RAILINGS

You came to watch me playing cricket once.
Quite a few of the fathers did.
At ease, outside the pavilion
they would while away a Saturday afternoon.
Joke with the masters, urge on
their flannelled offspring. But not you.

Fielding deep near the boundary
I saw you through the railings.
You were embarrassed when I waved
and moved out of sight down the road.
When it was my turn to bowl though
I knew you'd still be watching.

Third ball, a wicket, and three more followed.
When we came in at the end of the innings
the other dads applauded and joined us for tea.
Of course, you had gone by then. Later,
you said you'd found yourself there by accident.
Just passing. Spotted me through the railings.

\*    \*    \*

Speech-days · Prize-givings · School-plays
The Twentyfirst · The Wedding · The Christening
You would find yourself there by accident.
Just passing. Spotted me through the railings.

ROGER McGOUGH

# WALKING AWAY

It is eighteen years ago, almost to the day –
A sunny day with the leaves just turning,
The touch-lines new-ruled – since I watched you play
Your first game of football, then, like a satellite
Wrenched from its orbit, go drifting away

Behind a scatter of boys. I can see
You walking away from me towards the school
With the pathos of a half-fledged thing set free
Into a wilderness, the gait of one
Who finds no path where the path should be.

That hesitant figure, eddying away
Like a winged seed loosened from its parent stem,
Has something I never quite grasp to convey
About nature's give-and-take – the small, the scorching
Ordeals which fire one's irresolute clay.

I have had worse partings, but none that so
Gnaws at my mind still. Perhaps it is roughly
Saying what God alone could perfectly show –
How selfhood begins with a walking away,
And love is proved in the letting go.

**CECIL DAY LEWIS**

# A WISH FOR MY CHILDREN

On this doorstep I stand
year after year
to watch you going

and think: May you not
skin your knees. May you
not catch your fingers
in car doors. May
your hearts not break.

May tide and weather
wait for your coming

and may you grow strong
to break
all webs of my weaving.

**EVANGELINE PATERSON**

# I LOVE ME MUDDER

I love me mudder and me mudder love me
we come so far from over de sea
we heard dat de streets were paved with gold
sometime it hot sometime it cold,

I love me mudder and me mudder love me
we try fe live in harmony
you might know her as Valerie
but to me she is my mummy.

She shouts at me daddy so loud some time
she stays fit and she don't drink wine
she always do the best she can
she work damn hard down ina England,

she's always singing some kind of song
she have big muscles and she very very strong,
she likes pussy cats and she love cashew nuts
she don't bother with no ifs and buts.

I love me mudder and me mudder love me
we come so far from over de sea
we heard dat de streets were paved with gold
sometime it hot sometime it cold,

I love her and she love me too
and dis is a love I know is true
my family unit extends to you
loving each other is the ting to do

BENJAMIN ZEPHANIAH


## SQUEEZES

We love to squeeze bananas
We love to squeeze ripe plums
And when we're feeling sad
We love to squeeze our mums.

BRIAN PATTEN

# THE IRREPLACEABLE MUM

If you were a crack in the mirror,
If you were a flea on a cat,
If you were a slug in a jug,
I'd still love you, I wouldn't mind that.

If you were a smudge on a picture
Or an opera singer struck dumb,
If you were a pain in the neck then
You'd still be my very best chum.

If you were a fly in a pizza,
If you were a difficult sum,
Even if you were humpy and grumpy
You'd still be irreplaceable, Mum.

BRIAN PATTEN

# I WANT
# TO BE
# YOUR
# FRIEND

# AN EASY DECISION

I had finished my dinner
Gone for a walk
It was fine
Out and I started whistling

It wasn't long before

I met a
Man and his wife riding on
A pony with seven
Kids running along beside them

I said hello and
Went on
Pretty soon I met another
Couple
This time with nineteen
Kids and all of them
Riding on
A big smiling hippopotamus

I invited them home

**KENNETH PATCHEN**

# OATH OF FRIENDSHIP

*Shang ya!*
I want to be your friend
For ever and ever without break or decay.
When the hills are all flat
And the rivers are all dry,
When it lightens and thunders in winter,
When it rains and snows in summer,
When Heaven and Earth mingle –
Not till then will I part from you.

ANON (CHINA)

# ABOUT FRIENDS

The good thing about friends
is not having to finish sentences.

I sat a whole summer afternoon with my friend once
on a river bank, bashing heels on the baked mud
and watching the small chunks slide into the water
and listening to them – plop plop plop.
He said "I like the twigs when they . . . you know . . .
like that." I said "There's that branch . . ."
We both said "Mmmm." The river flowed and flowed
and there were lots of butterflies, that afternoon.

I first thought there was a sad thing about friends
when we met twenty years later.
We both talked hundreds of sentences,
taking care to finish all we said,
and explain it all very carefully,
as if we'd been discovered in places
we should not be, and were somehow ashamed.

I understood then what the river meant by flowing.

BRIAN JONES

# THE COMPETITION

At times the competition was fierce
between Cheri and me.
Had to be equal in all things.
Neither could bear
that the other could run
faster, pick a raspberry bush cleaner,
that the other's mind could scrape
the bottom of language, discover
the only seven-letter word
comprised entirely
of consonants.

Take skipping, take double dutch.
If she jumped 421 times without stopping
I'd jump 422, maybe 423, before collapsing
on the pavement.

Compared report cards, number of cavities,
valentines. Take boys.

*We don't need them, we've got each other.*

Dear Cheri: your cupped hands held me like water.
Can't remember when we began slipping
through each other's fingers.

PATRICIA YOUNG

## IT IS A PUZZLE

My friend
Is not my friend anymore.
She has secrets from me
And goes about with Tracy Hackett.

I would
Like to get her back,
Only do not want to say so.
So I pretend
To have secrets from her
And go about with Alice Banks.

But what bothers me is,
Maybe *she* is pretending
And would like *me* back,
Only does not want to say so.

In which case
Maybe it bothers her
That *I* am pretending.

But if we are both pretending,
Then really we are friends
And do not know it.

On the other hand,
How can we be friends
And have secrets from each other
And go about with other people?

My friend
Is not my friend anymore,
Unless she is pretending.
I cannot think what to do.
It is a puzzle.

ALLAN AHLBERG

# FRIENDS

I fear it's very wrong of me,
And yet I must admit,
When someone offers friendship
I want the *whole* of it.
I don't want everybody else
To share my friends with me.
At least, I want *one* special one,
Who, indisputably

Likes me much more than all the rest,
Who's always on my side,
Who never cares what others say,
Who lets me come and hide
Within his shadow, in his house –
It doesn't matter where –
Who lets me simply be myself,
Who's always, *always* there.

ELIZABETH JENNINGS

# SONNET

Guido, I wish that you and Lapo and I
Were carried off by magic
And put in a boat, which, every time there was a wind,
Would sail on the ocean exactly where we wanted.

In this way storms and other dangerous weather
Wouldn't be able to harm us –
And I wish that, since we all were of one mind,
We would want more and more to be together.

And I wish that Vanna and Lagia too
And the girl whose name on the list is number thirty
Were put in the boat by the magician too

And that we all did nothing but talk about love
And I wish that they were just as glad to be there
As I believe the three of us would be.

DANTE

# SECRET

Tell me your secret.
I promise not to tell.
I'll guard it safely at the bottom of a well.

Tell me your secret.
Tell me, tell me, please.
I won't breathe a word, not even to the bees.

Tell me your secret.
It will be a pebble in my mouth.
Not even the sea can make me spit it out.

JOHN AGARD

# BEYOND

Beyond this wooden
fence is only
moonlight on the water
tempting us
to keep our secret –

Moonlight, and a distant
drifting boat
which suddenly
becomes less lonely
as we kiss and tell.

JOHN MOLE

# RECUERDO

We were very tired, we were very merry –
We had gone back and forth all night on the ferry.
It was bare and bright, and smelled like a stable –
But we looked into a fire, we leaned across a table,
We lay on a hill-top underneath the moon;
And the whistles kept blowing, and the dawn came soon.

We were very tired, we were very merry –
We had gone back and forth all night on the ferry;
And you ate an apple, and I ate a pear,
From a dozen of each we had bought somewhere;
And the sky went wan, and the wind came cold,
And the sun rose dripping, a bucketful of gold.

We were very tired, we were very merry,
We had gone back and forth all night on the ferry.
We hailed, "Good morrow, mother!" to a shawl-covered head,
And bought a morning paper, which neither of us read;
And she wept, "God bless you!" for the apples and pears
And we gave her all our money but our subway fares.

EDNA ST VINCENT MILLAY

# TRAVEL

The railroad track is miles away,
    And the day is loud with voices speaking,
Yet there isn't a train goes by all day
    But I hear its whistle shrieking.

All night there isn't a train goes by,
    Though the night is still for sleep and dreaming
But I see its cinders red on the sky
    And hear its engine steaming.

My heart is warm with the friends I make,
    And better friends I'll not be knowing,
Yet there isn't a train I wouldn't take,
    No matter where it's going.

EDNA ST VINCENT MILLAY

# NIGHT JOURNEY

Now as the train bears west,
Its rhythm rocks the earth,
And from my Pullman berth
I stare into the night
While others take their rest.
Bridges of iron lace,
A suddenness of trees,
A lap of mountain mist
All cross my line of sight,
Then a bleak wasted place,
And a lake below my knees.
Full on my neck I feel
The straining at a curve;
My muscles move with steel,
I wake in every nerve.
I watch a beacon swing
From dark to blazing bright;
We thunder through ravines
And gullies washed with light.
Beyond the mountain pass
Mist deepens on the pane;
We rush into a rain
That rattles double glass.
Wheels shake the roadbed stone,
The pistons jerk and shove,
I stay up half the night
To see the land I love.

**THEODORE ROETHKE**

# THIS
# LAND
# IS ME

## THE WORLD IS
## DAY-BREAKING

The world is day-breaking!
The world is day-breaking!

Day arises
From its sleep.
Day wakes up
With the dawning light.

The world is day-breaking!
The world is day-breaking!

What are days for?
Days are where we live.
They come, they wake us
Time and time over.
They are to be happy in:
Where can we live but days?

The world is day-breaking!
The world is day-breaking!

SEKIYA MIYOSHI

120

# THESE HAVE I LOVED

These have I loved:
        White plates and cups, cleaning-gleaming,
Ringed with blue lines; and feathery, faery dust;
Wet roofs beneath the lamp-light; the strong crust
Of friendly bread; and many-tasting food;
Rainbows; and the blue bitter smoke of wood;
And radiant raindrops couching in cool flowers;
And flowers themselves, that sway through sunny hours,
Dreaming of moths that drink them under the moon . . .
Sweet water's dimpling laugh from tap or spring;
Holes in the ground; and voices that do sing:
Voices in laughter, too; and body's pain.

RUPERT BROOKE

# MIRACLES

Why, who makes much of a miracle?
As to me I know of nothing else but miracles,
Whether I walk the streets of Manhattan,
Or dart my sights over the roofs of houses toward the sky,
Or wade with naked feet along the beach just in the edge
    of the water,
Or stand under trees in the woods,
Or sit at table at dinner with the rest,
Or look at strangers opposite me riding in the car,
Or watch honey-bees busy around the hive of a summer
    forenoon,
Or animals feeding in the fields,
Or birds, or the wonderfulness of insects in the air,
Or the wonderfulness of the sundown, or the stars shining
    so quiet and bright,
Or the exquisite delicate thin curve of the new moon in
    spring;
These with the rest, one and all, are to me miracles,
The whole referring, yet each distinct and in its place.

To me every hour of the light and dark is a miracle,

Every cubic inch of space is a miracle,

Every square yard of the surface of the earth is spread
    with the same,

Every foot of the interior swarms with the same.


To me the sea is a continual miracle,

The fishes that swim – the rocks – the motion of the waves –
    the ships with men in them,

What stranger miracles are there?


WALT WHITMAN

# up into the silence

up into the silence the green
silence with a white earth in it

you will (kiss me) go

out into the morning the young
morning with a warm world in it

(kiss me) you will go

on into the sunlight the fine
sunlight with a firm day in it

you will go (kiss me

down into your memory and
a memory and memory

i) kiss me (will go)

**e. e. cummings**

# SONG FORM

Morning uptown, quiet on the street,
no matter the distinctions that can be
made, quiet, very quiet, on the street.
Sun's not even up, just some kid and me,
skating, both of us, at the early sun, and
amazed there is grace for us, without our
having to smile too tough, or be very pleasant
even to each other. Merely to be mere, ly to be

L e ROI JONES

# WE LIKE MARCH

We like March—his shoes are Purple.
He is new and high—
Makes he Mud for Dog and Peddler—
Makes he Forests Dry—
Knows the Adder's Tongue his coming
And begets her spot—
Stands the Sun so close and mighty—
That our Minds are hot.
News is he of all the others—
Bold it were to die
With the Blue Birds buccaneering
On his British sky—

EMILY DICKINSON

# AFTERNOON ON A HILL

I will be the gladdest thing
    Under the sun!
I will touch a hundred flowers
    And not pick one.

I will look at cliffs and clouds
    With quiet eyes,
Watch the wind bow down the grass,
    And the grass rise.

And when the lights begin to show
    Up from the town,
I will mark which must be mine,
    And then start down!

EDNA ST VINCENT MILLAY

## I THINK

I will write you a letter,
June day. Dear June Fifth,
you're all in green, so
many kinds and all one
green, tree shadows on
grass blades and grass
blade shadows. The air
fills up with motor
mower sound. The cat
walks up the drive
a dead baby rabbit
in her maw. The sun
is hot, the breeze
is cool. And suddenly
in all the green
the lilacs bloom,
massive and exquisite
in color and shape
and scent. The roses
are more full of
buds than ever. No
flowers. But soon.

June day, you have
your own perfection:
so green to say
goodbye to. Green,
stick around
a while.

JAMES SCHUYLER

## NOSEGAY

Violets, daffodils,
   roses and thorn
were all in the garden
   before you were born.

Daffodils, violets,
   red and white roses
your grandchildren's children
   will hold to their noses.

ELIZABETH COATSWORTH

# NO SHOP DOES THE BIRD USE

No shop does the bird use,
no counter nor baker,
but the bush is his orchard,
the grass is his acre,
the ant is his quarry,
the seed is his bread,
and a star is his candle
to light him to bed.

ELIZABETH COATSWORTH


## STAR–GAZER

The very stars are justified.
The galaxy
italicized.

I have proof-read
and proof-read
the beautiful script.

There are no
errors.

P. K. PAGE

# HOW MUCH?

How much do you love me, a million bushels?
Oh, a lot more than that, Oh, a lot more.

And tomorrow maybe only half a bushel?
Tomorrow maybe not even a half a bushel.

And is this your heart arithmetic?
This is the way the wind measures the weather.

CARL SANDBURG


# THUNDERSTORM IN THE FOURTH DRY SUMMER

Clouds hurled their silver spears
With a sound of thunder
But earth had hardened her shield
In fires of the sun.
Only the trees,
Dusty, weary and dying,
Clapped feeble hands
And pitifully cried for more.

NAN HUNT

# BRONZE AND SILVER

Look
Where the land lies,
Open like a book
Beneath these evening skies;
Still and clear
The stars of September appear
One by shimmering one,
The bronze day done.

Listen
How the birds sing
When the dew drops glisten,
The morning skies murmuring;
Soft and clear
The songs of September appear,
One by trembling one,
The silver day begun.

LEONARD CLARK

# SONG FOR THE SUN THAT DISAPPEARED BEHIND THE RAINCLOUDS

The fire darkens, the wood turns black.
The flame extinguishes, misfortune upon us.
God sets out in search of the sun.
The rainbow sparkles in his hand,
The bow of the divine hunter.
He has heard the lamentations of his children.
He walks along the milky way, he collects the stars.
With quick arms he piles them into a basket
Piles them up with quick arms
Like a woman who collects lizards
And piles them into her pot, piles them
Until the pot overflows with lizards
Until the basket overflows with light.

ANON (HOTTENTOT)

# THE KNOT IN THE WOOD

Thanks, and praise for
the knot in the wood

across the grain
making the carpenter curse

where a branch sprang out
carrying sap to each leaf.

GAEL TURNBULL

# TREE IN A STREET

Why will not that tree adapt itself to our tempo?
We have lopped off several branches,
cut her skin to the white bone,
run wires through her body and her loins,
yet she will not change.
Ignorant of traffic, of dynamos and steel,
as uncontemporary
as bloomers and bustles
she stands there like a green cliché.

LOUIS DUDEK

# IF TREES GUSHED BLOOD

If trees gushed blood
When they were felled
By meddling man,
And crimson welled

From every gash
His axe can give,
Would he forbear,
And let them live?

MERVYN PEAKE

## "WHY DID THEY KNOCK DOWN THE TREES, DADDY?"

It's a question of standards, boy; standards of living.
It's cars, you see, that give us a high level of living  –
help, so to speak, to set the thing in motion  –
and if they also give us a high level of dying
that's incidental, a fringe benefit, a lottery
likely to hand out unexpected promotion.

Without cars, let's face it, a nation is under-developed,
And these days it's bad to be under-developed in
anything at all  –
Bust, thighs, muscles, sex or ego,
It's a competitive world, son.

The trees? Oh, well they have to go
on the advice of Big Brother
so that the cars can have a better chance
of hitting one another.

COLIN THIELE

# THERE CAME A DAY

There came a day that caught the summer
Wrung its neck
Plucked it
And ate it.

Now what shall I do with the trees?
The day said, the day said.
Strip them bare, strip them bare.
Let's see what is really there.

And what shall I do with the sun?
The day said, the day said.
Roll him away till he's cold and small.
He'll come back rested if he comes back at all.

And what shall I do with the birds?
The day said, the day said.
The birds I've frightened, let them flit,
I'll hang out pork for the brave tomtit.

And what shall I do with the seed?
The day said, the day said.
Bury it deep, see what's its worth.
See if it can stand the earth.

What shall I do with the people?
The day said, the day said.
Stuff them with apple and blackberry pie –
They'll love me then till the day they die.

There came this day and he was autumn.
His mouth was wide
And red as a sunset.
His tail was an icicle.

TED HUGHES

# THE LONELY SCARECROW

My poor old bones  – I've only two –
A broomstick and a broken stave.
My ragged gloves are a disgrace.
My one peg-foot is in the grave.

I wear the labourer's old clothes:
Coat, shirt, and trousers all undone.
I bear my cross upon a hill
In rain and shine, in snow and sun.

I cannot help the way I look.
My funny hat is full of hay.
– O, wild birds, come and nest in me!
Why do you always fly away?

JAMES KIRKUP

# SNOW

In the gloom of whiteness,
In the great silence of snow,
A child was sighing
And bitterly saying: "Oh,
They have killed a white bird up there on her nest,
The down is fluttering from her breast."
And still it fell through that dusky brightness
On the child crying for the bird of the snow.

EDWARD THOMAS

# FEBRUARY TWILIGHT

I stood beside a hill
    Smooth with new-laid snow,
A single star looked out
    From the cold evening glow.

There was no other creature
    That saw what I could see –
I stood and watched the evening star
    As long as it watched me.

SARA TEASDALE

# THE MIRROR, THE SEA AND THE DARK, DARK WOOD

# PINE FOREST

The track cuts through the forest
Like a parting. Between the trees
It's dark, a place for gnomes
And goblins. Near the ground
A snow of grey-white fungus
Lives on leafless wood.


"Just a little way," you say
"Along this path." Pine needles
Inches deep, an island of fresh grass
Where there is sun. We're whispering
As if we were in church.
Ahead of us the tunnel reaches
Into blackness. I take your hand.

WENDY COPE

# FAIRY STORY

I went into the wood one day
And there I walked and lost my way

When it was so dark I could not see
A little creature came to me

He said if I would sing a song
The time would not be very long

But first I must let him hold my hand tight
Or else the wood would give me a fright

I sang a song, he let me go
But now I am home again there is nobody I know.

STEVIE SMITH

# THEY ASK:
# IS GOD, TOO, LONELY?

When God scooped up a handful of dust,
And spit on it, and molded the shape of man,
And blew a breath into it and told it to walk –
That was a great day.

And did God do this because He was lonely?
Did God say to Himself he must have company
And therefore He would make man to walk the earth
And set apart churches for speech and song with God?

These are questions.
They are scrawled in old caves.
They are painted in tall cathedrals.
There are men and women so lonely they believe
    God, too, is lonely.

CARL SANDBURG

# A SONG

My name is sweet Jenny, my age is sixteen
My father's a farmer on yonder green:
He's plenty of money to dress me in silk
But nae bonnie laddie will tak' me a walk.

I rose in the morning, I looked in the glass
I said to myself: What a handsome young lass!
My hands by my side and I gave a ha ha
But nae bonnie laddie will tak' me awa'.

ANON (SCOTLAND)

# STONE IN THE WATER

Stone in the water,
Stone on the sand,
Whom shall I marry
When I get to land?

Will he be handsome
Or will he be plain,
Strong as the sun
Or rich as the rain?

Will he be dark
Or will he be fair,
And what will be the colour
That shines in his hair?

Will he come late
Or will he come soon,
At morning or midnight
Or afternoon?

What will he say
Or what will he sing,
And will he be holding
A plain gold ring?

Stone in the water
Still and small,
Tell me if he comes,
Or comes not at all.

CHARLES CAUSLEY


## MIRROR POEM

If I look within the mirror,
Deep inside its frozen tears,
Shall I see the man I'll marry
Standing at my shoulder,
    Leaning down the years?

Shall I smile upon the mirror,
Shall my love look, smiling, back?
Midnight on Midsummer's eve:
What becomes of marriage
    If the glass should crack?

KIT WRIGHT

# MISS BLUES'ES CHILD

If the blues would let me,
Lord knows I would smile.
If the blues would let me,
I would smile, smile, smile.
Instead of that I'm cryin' –
I must be Miss Blues'es child.

You were my moon up in the sky,
At night my wishing star.
I love you, oh, I love you so –
But you have gone so far!

Now my days are lonely,
And night-time drives me wild.
In my heart I'm crying,
I'm just Miss Blues'es child!

LANGSTON HUGHES

# MONOLOGUE

Mother, will you come
And kiss away my fear,
Every night like this night?
Yes, I will come, my dear.

Tomorrow – do not cry –
Flowers I will bring,
And our secret lullaby
In your ears I'll sing.

Now sleep. Hard shines the moon,
And I must go.
Your narrow bed will soon
Be white with snow.

ALUN LEWIS

# A FROSTY NIGHT

"Alice, dear, what ails you,
    Dazed and lost and shaken?
Has the chill night numbed you?
    Is it fright you have taken?"

"Mother, I am very well,
    I was never better.
Mother, do not hold me so,
    Let me write my letter."

"Sweet, my dear, what ails you?"
    "No, but I am well.
The night was cold and frosty –
    There's no more to tell."

"Ay, the night was frosty,
    Coldly gaped the moon,
Yet the birds seemed twittering
    Through green boughs of June.

"Soft and thick the snow lay,
    Stars danced in the sky –
Not all the lambs of May-day
    Skip so bold and high.

"Your feet were dancing, Alice,
    Seemed to dance on air,
You looked a ghost or angel
    In the star-light there.

"Your eyes were frosted star-light;
    Your heart, fire and snow.
Who was it said, 'I love you'?"
    "Mother, let me go!"

ROBERT GRAVES

# SOMETIMES IT HAPPENS

And sometimes it happens that you are friends and then
You are not friends,
And friendship has passed.
And whole days are lost and among them
A fountain empties itself.

And sometimes it happens that you are loved and then
You are not loved,
And love is past.
And whole days are lost and among them
A fountain empties itself into the grass.

And sometimes you want to speak to her and then
You do not want to speak,
Then the opportunity has passed.
Your dreams flare up, they suddenly vanish.

And also it happens that there is nowhere to go and then
There is somewhere to go,
Then you have bypassed.
And the years flare up and are gone,
Quicker than a minute.

So you have nothing.

You wonder if these things matter and then

As soon as you begin to wonder if these things matter

They cease to matter,

And caring is past.

And a fountain empties itself into the grass.

BRIAN PATTEN

## THE FOUNTAINS

Suddenly all the fountains in the park

Opened smoothly their umbrellas of water,

Yet there was none but me to miss or mark

Their peacock show, and so I moved away

Uneasily, like one who at a play

Finds himself all alone, and will not stay.

W. R. RODGERS

# MY TRUE LOVE

On Monday, Monday,
  My True Love said to me,
"I've brought you this nice pumpkin;
  I picked it off a tree!"

On Tuesday, Tuesday,
  My True Love said to me,
"Look – I've brought you sand tarts;
  I got them by the sea."

On Wednesday, Wednesday,
  My True Love said to me,
"I've caught you this white polar bear;
  It came from Tennessee."

On Thursday, Thursday,
  My True Love said to me,
"This singing yellow butterfly
  I've all for you, from me."

On Friday, Friday,
    My True Love said to me,
"Here's a long-tailed guinea pig;
    It's frisky as can be."

On Saturday, Saturday,
    To my True Love I said,
"You have not told me ONE TRUE THING,
    So you I'll never wed!"

IVY O. EASTWICK

## MIRROR, MIRROR, TELL ME

Mirror, mirror, tell me,
    Am I pretty or plain?
Or am I downright ugly
    And ugly to remain?
Shall I marry a gentleman?
    Shall I marry a clown?
Or shall I marry old Knives and Scissors
    Shouting through the town?

ANON

157

# LOWER THE DIVER

Lower the diver over the side
Down to the roots of the swirling tide.

Lower the diver, weighted with lead,
Glass and brass helmet over his head.

Lower the diver on to the deck
And the barnacled masts of the long-lost wreck.

Lower the diver; will he find jars,
Rust-sealed treasure-chests, silver bars?

Lower the diver; will he find gold,
Cannon-balls, skulls, or an empty hold?

Lower the diver; pray that the shark
Doesn't mind guests in the salty dark.

Lower the diver; then man the winch,
Wind him up slowly, inch by inch.

Undo his helmet. Why does he weep?
Is it so bad to be hauled from the deep?

Talk to the diver. What does he mean –
"mermaids are real and her eyes were green"?

RICHARD EDWARDS


## THE MERMAID

A mermaid found a swimming lad,
Picked him for her won,
Pressed her body to his body,
Laughed, and plunging down
Forgot in cruel happiness
That even lovers drown.

W. B. YEATS

## *from* THE LOVE SONG OF
## J. ALFRED PRUFROCK

I grow old . . . I grow old . . .
I shall wear the bottoms of my trousers rolled.

Shall I part my hair behind? Do I dare to eat a peach?
I shall wear white flannel trousers, and walk upon the beach.
I have heard the mermaids singing, each to each.

I do not think that they will sing to me.

I have seen them riding seaward on the waves
Combing the white hair of the waves blown back
When the wind blows the water white and black.

We have lingered in the chambers of the sea
By sea-girls wreathed with seaweed red and brown
Till human voices wake us, and we drown.

T. S. ELIOT

# JENNY KISS'D ME

Jenny kiss'd me when we met,
    Jumping from the chair she sat in;
Time, you thief, who love to get
    Sweets into your list, put that in!
Say I'm weary, say I'm sad,
    Say that health and wealth have miss'd me,
Say I'm growing old, but add,
    Jenny kiss'd me.

LEIGH HUNT


# THE INVISIBLE MAN

The girl who felt my stare and raised her eyes
Saw I was only an old man, and looked away,
As people do when they see something not quite nice
Or a row of houses so dreary they'll spoil your day.

Children don't see me at all: they look right through me
My sons reach out a filial helping hand
(To me, who am shaking now with lust and fury).
These facts I know but find it difficult to understand.

T. S. MATTHEWS

# WHEN YOU SEE ME
# SITTING QUIETLY

When you see me sitting quietly,
Like a sack left on the shelf,
Don't think I need your chattering,
I'm listening to myself.
Hold! Stop! Don't pity me!
Hold! Stop your sympathy!
Understanding if you got it,
Otherwise I'll do without it!

When my bones are stiff and aching
And my feet won't climb the stairs,
I will only ask one favour:
Don't bring me no rocking-chair.

When you see me walking, stumbling,
Don't study and get it wrong.
'Cause tired don't mean lazy
And every goodbye ain't gone.
I'm the same person I was back then,
A little less hair, a little less chin,
A lot less lungs and much less wind,
But ain't I lucky I can still breathe in.

MAYA ANGELOU

# DO NOT DESPISE ME

Please do not despise me if I am
too old in the head and shoulders
too inadequately schooled
in the ins and outs of today
but since I've lived three score years
and am not high or low
wise or wealthy, I would
be grateful if I'm just accepted
as your other grandmother
who cannot speak English

KONAI HELU THAMAN

# THE LODGER

I used to live all by myself
Like a rusty tea caddy on a shelf.

My head is bald, I'm an old crone,
I used to live by myself alone.

And ROOM TO LET the window said,
But no one creaked on the iron bed.

At the end of the year a stranger came,
He took the room, he gave no name.

He is silent and sly, he is up to no good,
He looks through chinks as no gentleman should;

He has hidden the gold-edged chamberpot,
He has been at the cheese, he takes the lot.

No use to hide anything or lock it,
He has pinched the only bulb from its socket!

One day, when I lie chill in my bed,
He will put the pillow over my head,

Pull down the blinds, switch off the day,
Pocket my eyes and walk away.

GERDA MAYER

# BEAUTIFUL OLD AGE

It ought to be lovely to be old
to be full of the peace that comes of experience
and wrinkled ripe fulfilment.

The wrinkled smile of completeness that follows a life
lived undaunted and unsoured with accepted lies.
If people lived without accepting lies
they would ripen like apples, and be scented like pippins
in their old age.

Soothing, old people should be, like apples
when one is tired of love.
Fragrant like yellowing leaves, and dim with the soft
stillness and satisfaction of autumn.

And a girl should say:
It must be wonderful to live and grow old.
Look at my mother, how rich and still she is! –

And a young man should think: By Jove
my father has faced all weathers, but it's been a life! –

D. H. LAWRENCE

## WARNING

When I am an old woman I shall wear purple
With a red hat which doesn't go, and doesn't suit me,
And I shall spend my pension on brandy and summer gloves
And satin sandals, and say we've no money for butter.
I shall sit down on the pavement when I'm tired
And gobble up samples in shops and press alarm bells
And run my stick along the public railings
And make up for the sobriety of my youth.
I shall go out in my slippers in the rain
And pick the flowers in other people's gardens
And learn to spit.

You can wear terrible shirts and grow more fat
And eat three pounds of sausages at a go
Or only bread and pickle for a week
And hoard pens and pencils and beermats and things in boxes.

But now we must have clothes that keep us dry
And pay the rent and not swear in the street
And set a good example for the children.
We must have friends to dinner and read the papers.

But maybe I ought to practise a little now?
So people who know me are not too shocked and surprised
When suddenly I am old and start to wear purple.

JENNY JOSEPH

# ME AS MY GRANDMOTHER

Sometimes
I look up quickly
and see for an instant
her face
in my mirror,
random tightness
turns my mouth
into a facsimile of hers,
eyes caught oddly
in the glass
make me
into her
looking at me.

Now that she's dead,
I understand
that it is right
that I should age
and wrinkle into her.

It brings her back,
it puts me into
the cycle of family.
We look at all time
with just that
one same face.

**ROSEMARY AUBERT**

# WELL CAUGHT

These days I'm in love with
    my face.
It has grown round and
    genial as I've become older.
In it I see my grandfather's face and
    that
Of my mother. Yes – like a ball it
    has been thrown
From one generation to the next.

GERDA MAYER

# AND
# WILL THE
# FLOWERS
# DIE?

## POEM FROM A
## THREE-YEAR-OLD

And will the flowers die?

And will the people die?

And every day do you grow old, do I
grow old, no I'm not old, do
flowers grow old?

Old things – do you throw them out?

Do you throw old people out?

And how you know a flower that's old?

The petals fall, the petals fall from flowers,
and do the petals fall from people too,
every day more petals fall until the
floor where I would like to play I
want to play is covered with old
flowers and people all the same
together lying there with petals fallen

on the dirty floor I want to play
the floor you come and sweep
with the huge broom.

The dirt you sweep, what happens that,
what happens all the dirt you sweep
from flowers and people, what
happens all the dirt? Is all the
dirt what's left of flowers and
people, all the dirt there in a
heap under the huge broom that
sweeps everything away?

Why you work so hard, why brush
and sweep to make a heap of dirt?

And who will bring new flowers?

And who will bring new people? Who will
bring new flowers to put in water
where no petals fall on to the
floor where I would like to
play? Who will bring new flowers
that will not hang their heads
like tired old people wanting sleep?

Who will bring new flowers that
do not split and shrivel every
day? And if we have new flowers,
will we have new people too to
keep the flowers alive and give
them water?

And will the new young flowers die?

And will the new young people die?

And why?

BRENDAN KENNELLY

# HE WAS JEALOUS

He was jealous, worried and tender,
like God's sun he loved me.
He killed my white bird
to stop it singing of the past.

Coming into the room at sunset, he said:
"Love me, laugh, write poetry!"
I buried the happy bird
beyond the round well near the old alder tree.

I promised him not to cry.
But my heart turned to stone,
and it seems that always, and everywhere
I will hear its sweet voice.

ANNA AKHMATOVA

# DREAMPOEM

in a corner of my bedroom
    grew a tree
    a happytree
    my own tree
its leaves were soft
    like flesh
and its birds sang poems for me
then
    without warning
two men
    with understanding smiles
and axes
    made out of forged excuses
came and chopped it down
either                  yesterday
    or the day before
i think it was the day before

ROGER McGOUGH

# DREAMS

Hold fast to dreams
For if dreams die
Life is a broken-winged bird
That cannot fly.

Hold fast to dreams
For when dreams go
Life is a barren field
Frozen with snow.

**LANGSTON HUGHES**

# TRACEY'S TREE

Last year it was not there,
the sapling with purplish leaves
planted in our school grounds with care.
It is Tracey's tree, my friend who died,
and last year it was not there.

Tracey, the girl with long black hair
who, out playing one day, ran
across a main road for a dare.
The lorry struck her. Now a tree grows
and last year it was not there.

Through the classroom window I stare
and watch the sapling sway.
Soon its branches will stand bare.
It wears a forlorn and lonely look
and last year it was not there.

October's chill is in the air
and cold rain distorts my view.
I feel a sadness that's hard to bear.
The tree blurs, as if I've been crying,
and last year it was not there.

WES MAGEE

178

# MY SISTER

My little sister died last night
In the hospital.
She was four days old.
Only four days old.
And when I saw her for the first time
I don't think I'd ever been as happy.
She was so small and crinkled
With big eyes and soft soft skin.
And a smile like a rainbow.
Her fingers were like tiny sticks
and her nails like little sea shells
And her hair like white feathers.
Now she's gone, and my mum can't
      stop crying.
And my dad stares at nothing.
I loved our baby.
I'll never forget her.

*JAMES TOOHEY (aged 11)*

# WHEN I AM DEAD

When I am dead
Cry for me a little
Think of me sometimes
But not too much.
Think of me now and again
As I was in life
At some moments it's pleasant to recall
But not for long.
Leave me in peace
And I shall leave you in peace
And while you live
Let your thoughts be with the living.

ANON (INDIA)

# THE BUSTLE IN A HOUSE

The Bustle in a House
The Morning after Death
Is solemnest of industries
Enacted upon earth—

The Sweeping up the Heart,
And putting Love away
We shall not want to use again
Until Eternity.

EMILY DICKINSON

# THE DUST OF LOVERS

The wheel of Fate is crooked. It destroys
    Such innocent young souls as yours and mine:
So, joyously sit down upon the grass
    And while away this hour in drinking wine.
Alas! the meadow which delights our eyes,
    On which you now recline your lovely head,
Is rooted in the dust of lovers – and
    Will spring from ours one day when we are dead.

**OMAR KHAYÝAM**

# POST-SCRIPT:
# FOR GWENO

If I should go away,
Beloved, do not say
"He has forgotten me".
For you abide,
A singing rib within my dreaming side;
You always stay.
And in the mad tormented valley
Where blood and hunger rally
And Death the wild beast is uncaught, untamed,
Our soul withstands the terror
And has its quiet honour
Among the glittering stars your voices named.

ALUN LEWIS

# LITTLE BOY BLUE

The little toy dog is covered with dust,
    But sturdy and staunch he stands,
And the little toy soldier is red with rust,
    And his musket moulds in his hands.
Time was when the little toy dog was new,
    And the soldier was passing fair;
And that was the time when our Little Boy Blue
    Kissed them and put them there.

"Now, don't you go till I come," he said,
    "And don't you make any noise!"
So, toddling off to his trundle-bed,
    He dreamt of the pretty toys;
And, as he was dreaming, an angel song
    Awakened our Little Boy Blue –
Oh! the years are many, the years are long,
    But the little toy friends are true!

Aye, faithful to Little Boy Blue they stand,
    Each in the same old place –
Awaiting the touch of a little hand,
    The smile of a little face;
And they wonder, as waiting the long years through
    In the dust of the little chair,
What has become of our Little Boy Blue,
    Since he kissed them and put them there.

EUGENE FIELD

# STOP ALL THE CLOCKS

Stop all the clocks, cut off the telephone,
Prevent the dog from barking with a juicy bone,
Silence the pianos and with muffled drum
Bring out the coffin, let the mourners come.

Let aeroplanes circle moaning overhead
Scribbling on the sky the message He Is Dead,
Put crêpe bows round the white necks of the public doves,
Let the traffic policemen wear black cotton gloves.

He was my North, my South, my East and West,
My working week and my Sunday rest,
My noon, my midnight, my talk, my song;
I thought that love would last for ever: I was wrong.

The stars are not wanted now: put out every one;
Pack up the moon and dismantle the sun;
Pour away the ocean and sweep up the wood.
For nothing now can ever come to any good.

W. H. AUDEN

# OF NOTHING AT ALL: ORDERS

Muffle the wind;
Silence the clock;
Muzzle the mice;
Curb the small talk;
Cure the hinge-squeak;
Banish the thunder.
Let me sit silent,
Let me wonder.

A. M. KLEIN

# TELEPHONE

Telephone told me that you were dead
Now I hate every telephone's stupid head
I'd rather sit here turning to a block of stone
Than pick up any snake of a telephone.

ADRIAN MITCHELL

# THERE ARE SOME MEN

There are some men
who should have mountains
to bear their names to time.

Grave-markers are not high enough
or green,
and sons go far away
to lose the fist
their father's hand will always seem.

I had a friend:
he lived and died in mighty silence
and with dignity,
left no book, son, or lover to mourn.

Nor is this a mourning-song
but only a naming of this mountain
on which I walk,
fragrant, dark, and softly white
under the pale of mist.
I name this mountain after him.

LEONARD COHEN

## LINES ON A CLOCK IN CHESTER CATHEDRAL

When as a child, I laughed and wept,
    Time crept.
When as a youth, I dreamt and talked,
    Time walked.
When I became a full-grown man,
    Time ran.
When older still I daily grew,
    Time flew.
Soon I shall find on travelling on –
    Time gone.
O Christ, wilt Thou have saved me then?
    Amen.

HENRY TWELLS

## I HAVE LIVED
## AND I HAVE LOVED

I have lived and I have loved;
I have waked and I have slept;
I have sung and I have danced;
I have smiled and I have wept;
I have won and wasted treasure;
I have had my fill of pleasure;
And all these things were weariness,
And some of them were dreariness.
And all these things – but two things
Were emptiness and pain:
And Love – it was the best of them:
And Sleep – worth all the rest of them.

ANON

# BUFFALO DUSK

The buffaloes are gone.

And those who saw the buffaloes are gone.

Those who saw the buffaloes by thousands and how they
    pawed the prairie sod into dust with their hoofs,
    their great heads down pawing on in a great pageant
    of dusk,

Those who saw the buffaloes are gone.

And the buffaloes are gone.

CARL SANDBURG

# FAREWELL

A little while
and
I will be gone from among you,
whither I cannot tell.
From nowhere we come;
into nowhere we go.

What is life?
It is a flash of a firefly
in the night.
It is a breath of a buffalo
in the winter time.
It is the little shadow
that runs across the grass
and loses itself in the sunset.

CHIEF CROWFOOT

# EVERYTHING TOUCHES

## THE SONG OF
## CHIEF KORUINKA

The whole earth is one spirit,
we are a part of it.
Our spirits cannot die.
They face changes, certainly,
but not extinction.
We are all one spirit,
just as there is only one world.

**CHIEF KORUINKA**

# THE BUBBLE RING

When I was young,
   I did a thing
With liquid soap
   And a bubble ring:

I swished it deep
   And then I blew
And iridescent
   Bubbles grew

And drifted up
   To nudge the air,
Leaving a mental
   Shimmer there.

And though my childhood
   Days are gone,
That funny lift
   Of light goes on –

For when the world
   Is rife again
With news of war
   And acid rain,

Or when my will
    Is clenched and fraught
With worry lines
    Of *is* and *ought*,

I often sit
    And watch the way
New bubbles rise
    In the mind's display.

Sometimes they frisk
    Along in flight,
And ask no more
    Than sheer delight;

Sometimes they seem
    A concentrate
Of good and evil,
    Mean and great –

Till drifting through
    The world I see
Bright bubbles
    Of eternity.

And as they trace
    Their little course,
I feel my will
    Resume its force,

For images
    Of clean desire
Incite us like
    Refining fire,

And though the bubbles
    Disappear,
They leave a living
    Shimmer here.

DENNIS LEE

# FULL CIRCLE WORLD

Good morning dear world,
So briefly known.
In flashes only seen,
So often missed
By eyes so self-obsessed.
Good morning dear earth,
With your clouds like flags unfurled
And your sun that walks on beams of frost
And lights all we thought lost.
Good morning dear mist,
Dear floating lakes of light through which
The numbed bee and its cargo sails.
Good morning dear sky,
Dear scented woven threads of air
That blow away despair
From this world so briefly known,
In flashes only seen,
So often missed
By eyes so self-obsessed.
Good morning dear world.

BRIAN PATTEN

# NATIONALITY

I have grown past hate and bitterness,
I see the world as one;
But though I can no longer hate,
my son is still my son.

All men at God's round table sit,
And all men must be fed;
But this loaf in my hand,
This loaf is my son's bread.

MARY GILMORE


# 'TIL THE END OF TIME

'Til the end of time
my love for you will never leave you,
'til the end of time,
until the end of time.

Through the darkest night
my  love for you will never leave you,
through the darkest night,
throughout the darkest night.

FRANCESCA LEFTLEY
(based on Isaiah 54:10)

## YES

A smile says: Yes
A heart says: Blood.
When the rain says: Drink
The earth says: Mud.

The kangaroo says: Trampoline.
Giraffes say: Tree.
A bus says: Us
While a car says: Me.

Lemon trees say: Lemons.
A jug says: Lemonade.
The villain says: You're wonderful.
The hero: I'm afraid.

The forest says: Hide and Seek.
The grass says: Green and Grow.
The railway says: Maybe.
The prison says: No.

The millionaire says: Take.
The beggar says: Give.
The soldier cries: Mother!
The baby sings: Live.

The river says: Come with me.

The moon says: Bless.

The stars say: Enjoy the light.

The sun says: Yes.

**ADRIAN MITCHELL**

## SING A SONG
## OF PEOPLE

Sing a song of people
    Walking fast or slow;
People in the city,
    Up and down they go.

People on the sidewalk,
People on the bus;
People passing, passing,
In back and front of us.
People on the subway
Underneath the ground;
People riding taxis
Round and round and round.

People with their hats on,
Going in the doors;
People with umbrellas
When it rains and pours.
People in tall buildings
And in stores below;
Riding elevators
Up and down they go.

People walking singly,
People in a crowd;
People saying nothing,
People talking loud.
People laughing, smiling,
Grumpy people too;
People who just hurry
And never look at you!

Sing a song of people
    Who like to come and go;
Sing of city people
    You see but never know!

LOIS LENSKI

## THIS IS EVERYTHING, TOO
## —REPLY TO A YOUNG FRIEND

Not all giant trees
    Are broken by the storm;
Not all seeds
    Find no soil to strike root;
Not all true feelings
    Vanish in the desert of man's heart;
Not all dreams
    Allow their wings to be clipped.

No, not everything
    Ends as you foretold!

Not all flames
    Burn themselves out
    Without sparking off others;
Not all stars
    Indicate the night
    Without predicting the dawn;
Not all songs
    Brush past the ears
    Without remaining in the heart.

No, not everything
    Ends as you foretold!

Not all appeals
    Receive no response;
Not all losses
    Are beyond retrieval;
Not all abysses
    Mean destruction;
Not all destruction
    Falls on the weak;

Not all souls
    Can be ground underfoot
    And turned into putrid mud;
Not all consequences
    Are streaked with tears and blood
    And do not show a smiling face.

Everything present is pregnant with the future,
Everything future comes from the past.
Have hope, struggle for it,
Bear these on your shoulders.

SHU TING

# I WILL NEVER FORGET YOU, MY PEOPLE

I will never forget you, my people;
I have carved you on the palm of my hand.
I will never forget you;
I will not leave you orphaned.
I will never forget my own.

Does a mother forget her baby?
Or a woman the child within her womb?
Yet even if these forget,
Yes, even if these forget,
I will never forget my own.

CAREY LANDRY
*(based on Isaiah 49:15ff)*

# EVERYTHING TOUCHES

Everything touches, life interweaves
Starlight and gunsmoke, ashes and leaves
Birdsong and thunder, acid and rain
Everything touches, unbroken chain

Chainsaw and rainbow, warrior and priest
Assassin off-duty, beauty and beast
Heartbeat and hightide, ebb and flow
Cardboard cathedral covered in snow

Snowdrop and gangrene, hangman and clown
Walls that divide come tumbling down
Seen though the night the glimmer of day
Light is but darkness worn away

Past and future, distance and time
Atom to atom, water to wine
Look all around, what do you see?
Everything touches, you're touching me

Look all around, what do you see?
Everything touches, you're touching me.

**ROGER McGOUGH**

# WHERE THE CIRCLE BEGINS

who can find out
where the river ends?

who knows where
this street leads to?

who waits outside
the outskirts of death?

a strange landmark
this silence
        trapped
within silence
within silence

who knows where
the circle begins?

**PRITISH NANDY**

# INDEX OF POETS

# INDEX OF TITLES
# AND FIRST LINES

Titles are in *italics*. Where the title and the first line are the same, the first line only is listed.

220

# ACKNOWLEDGEMENTS

The publisher would like to thank the copyright holders for permission to reproduce the following copyright material:

**John Agard**: John Agard and Caroline Sheldon Literary Agency for "Telephone" and "Secret" from *Get Back Pimple*, Viking 1996. Copyright © 1996 John Agard. **Allan Ahlberg**: Penguin Books for "It Is A Puzzle" from *Please Mrs Butler*, Viking 1984. Copyright © 1994 Allan Ahlberg. **Maya Angelou**: Little, Brown & Company (UK) for "On Ageing" from *Shaker Why Don't You Sing?*, Virago 1986. Copyright © 1986 Maya Angelou. **Rosemary Aubert**: Oberon Press for "Me As My Grandmother" from *Two Kinds of Honey*, Oberon Press. Copyright © Rosemary Aubert. **W. H. Auden**: Faber & Faber Ltd for an extract from "As I Walked Out One Evening", "Some Say That Love's a Little Boy" and "Stop All the Clocks" from "Twelve Songs" from *Collected Poems of W. H. Auden* edited by Edward Mendelson, Faber & Faber Ltd. Copyright © 1940 and renewed 1968 by W. H. Auden. **Sebastian Barker**: Enitharmon Press for "A Love Song to Eros" from *The Hand in the Well*, Enitharmon Press 1966. Copyright © 1966 Sebastian Barker. **Hilaire Belloc**: The Peters, Fraser & Dunlop Group Ltd for "Juliet" and "The Fragment" from *Complete Verse* by Hilaire Belloc, Random House. **Charles Causley**: David Higham Associates for "Give Me A House" from *Jack the Treacle Eater*, Viking Kestrel and "Stone in the Water" from *Early In The Morning*, Viking Kestrel. Copyright © Charles Causley. **Leonard Clark**: The Literary Executor of Leonard Clark (1905-1981) for "Bronze and Silver" from *Good Company* by Leonard Clark, Dobson Books. **Leonard Cohen**: Random House UK Ltd for "There Are Some Men" from *Poems 1956-1969* by Leonard Cohen, Jonathan Cape 1969. Copyright © 1969 Leonard Cohen. **Tony Connor**: Anvil Press Poetry for "A Child Half-asleep". Copyright © Tony Connor. **Wendy Cope**: Faber & Faber Ltd for "Valentine" and "The Orange" from *Serious Concerns*, Faber & Faber Ltd 1992. Copyright © 1992 Wendy Cope. **Robert Creeley**: Marion Boyars Publishers Ltd for "Love Comes Quietly" from *Poems 1950-65* by Robert Creeley, Marion Boyars Publishers Ltd. Copyright © Robert Creeley. **e. e. cummings**: W. W. Norton & Co. Inc. for "up into the silence green" from *Complete Poems* by e. e. cummings, Grafton Books. **Diane Dawber**: Borealis Press Ltd for "Zeroing In" from *Oatmeal Mittens*, Borealis Press 1987. Copyright © 1987 Diane Dawber. **Louis Dudek**: the author for "Tree In A Street" from *Selected Poems* by Louis Dudek, Golden Dog Press 1975. Copyright © 1975 Louis Dudek. **Carol Ann Duffy**: Anvil Press Poetry Ltd for "Words Wide Night" and "Who Loves You" from *The Other Country*, Anvil Press 1990. Copyright © 1990 Carol Ann Duffy. **Douglas Dunn**: Faber & Faber Ltd for "To My Daughter" from *Terry Street*, Faber & Faber Ltd. Copyright © Douglas Dunn. **Richard Edwards**: Penguin Books Ltd for "Lower the Diver", "The Glove and the Guitar" and "Samooreena" from *The House That Caught A Cold*, Viking. Copyright © Richard Edwards. **T. S. Eliot**: Faber & Faber Ltd for 12 lines from "The Love Song of J. Alfred Prufrock" from *Collected Poems 1909-1962*, Faber & Faber Ltd. Copyright © T. S. Eliot. **Mari Evans**: William Morrow & Co. for "Where Have You Gone" from *I Am A Black Woman*, William Morrow & Co. 1970. Copyright © 1970 Mari Evans. **Eleanor Farjeon**: David Higham Associates Ltd for "The Quarrel" from *Silver Sand and Snow*, Michael Joseph. Copyright © Eleanor Farjeon. **Linda France**: Bloodaxe Books Ltd for "If Love Was Jazz" from *Red*, Bloodaxe Books Ltd, 1992. Copyright © 1992 Linda France. **Nikki Giovanni**: Farrar, Straus & Giroux Inc. for "Poem for Ntombe Iayo (At Five Weeks of Age)" from *Spin a Soft Black Song*, Farrar Straus & Giroux Inc. 1971. Copyright © 1971 Nikki Giovanni. **Robert Graves**: Carcanet Press for "A Frosty Night" by Robert Graves. Copyright © Robert Graves. **E. Y. Harburg**: International Music Publications Ltd for "Down With Love", lyrics E. Y. Harburg, music H. Arlen. Copyright 1937 Chappell & Co. Ltd. **Mike Harding**: Peterloo Poets for "Dancing On My Toes" from *Daddy Edgar's Pools*, Peterloo Poets 1992. Copyright © 1992 Mike Harding. **John Hegley**: The Peters Fraser & Dunlop Group Ltd for "Love Poems" from *Love Cuts*, Methuen. Copyright © John Hegley. **Adrian Henri**: The author c/o Rogers, Coleridge & White Ltd for "Adrian Henri's Talking After Christmas Blues" and "Song For A Beautiful Girl Petrol-Pump Attendant On The Motorway" from *Collected Poems* by Adrian Henri, Alison & Busby 1986. Copyright © 1986 Adrian Henri. **Libby Houston**: the author for "A Good Idea For Wintry Weather" from *All Change*, OUP. Copyright © Libby Houston. **Langston**